THIS WALKER BOOK BELONGS TO:

Su-min

Kim 2G

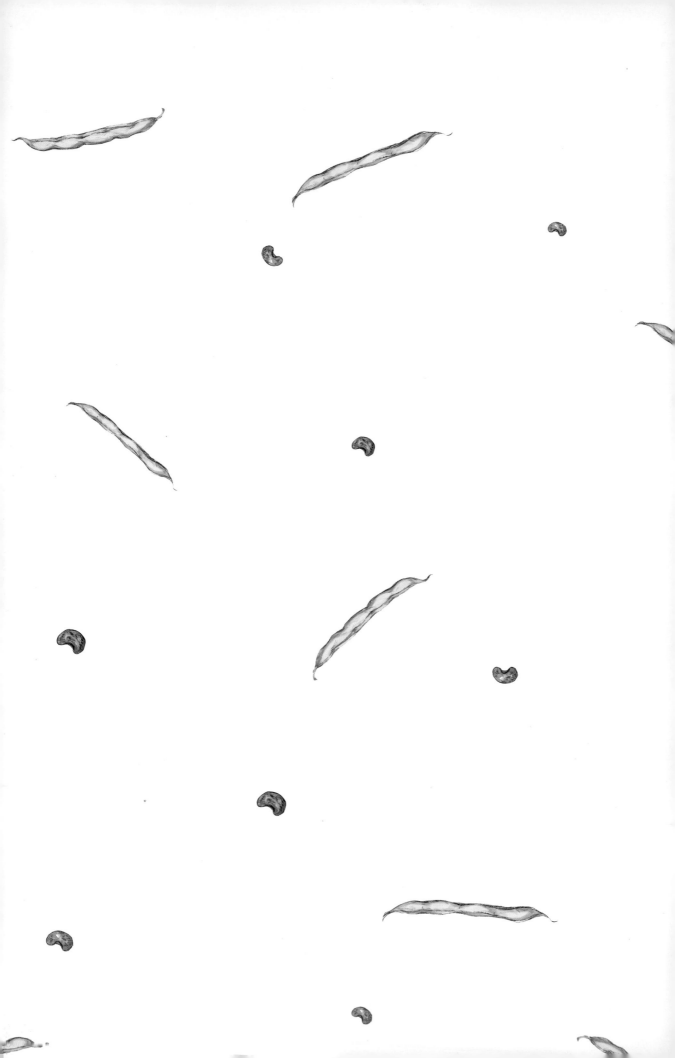

For Liz, with all my love
M.J.D.

With thanks to Walker Books
J.A.

First published 1999
by Walker Books Ltd
87 Vauxhall Walk
London SE11 5HJ

This edition published 2002

2 4 6 8 10 9 7 5 3

Text © 1999 Malachy Doyle
Illustrations © 1999 Judith Allibone

This book has been typeset in Usherwood

Printed in Hong Kong

British Library Cataloguing in Publication Data:
a catalogue record for this book is
available from the British Library

ISBN 0-7445-6281-3

JODY'S BEANS

Malachy Doyle

illustrated by Judith Allibone

WALKER BOOKS

AND SUBSIDIARIES

LONDON • BOSTON • SYDNEY

It was springtime, and Jody's Granda
came to visit.

He brought Jody a packet of runner beans.

They counted them out on
the kitchen table.

"...nine, ten, eleven, twelve," said Granda.

"That's enough."

They went out into the garden and found
the sunniest spot where the wind never blew.

They dug the soil and pulled out
all the weeds, mixed in some compost
and raked it over.

Then Jody made twelve holes in a circle,
and put one seed in each.

"Don't forget to
water them, Jody,"
said Granda.

"What do runner beans look like,
Granda?" asked Jody.

"Wait and see,"
said Granda.
"Wait and see."

9

Soon the tiny green plants pushed their way
up through the dark brown soil.

Jody watered them
every day, unless it rained,
just as she'd been told.

One day the phone rang. It was Granda.

"Hello, Jody," he said.
"How are the beans?"

"They're growing
fast," said Jody.

"Good," said Granda. "Now listen closely.
This is what I want you to do..."

Jody went down to her vegetable patch
and pulled out the smallest plants.
Now the strongest ones
had plenty of room to grow.

Soon they were as

tall as the cat.

When Granda came to visit again,

he pushed six long canes in the ground beside

the plants, and tied them together at the top.

He looped string round and round

the poles all the way up

from the bottom.

"It's like
a wigwam,"
said Jody.

The next few weeks were hot.

The sun burned down on the garden.

Jody watered her plants every day.

They snaked up the wigwam,

hooking themselves on to the string

as they went.

"Granda," she said on the phone,
"they're bigger than me now!"

"That's great, Jody,"
said Granda.

"How big will
they get?"
Jody asked.

"Wait and see," said Granda.
"Wait and see."

 17

 Then the rain came.

Lots and lots of it.

Jody hardly had to water the plants at all.

They grew bigger every day,
and bright red flowers
burst out all over them.

"They're so beautiful,
Dad," said Jody.

After the warm
sunny days returned
the first beans
appeared.

The plants reached the

tops of the poles, and Granda
came to visit again.

"They're even taller
than you, Granda!"
said Jody.

"They're wonderful beans, Jody,"
Granda said, pinching the tips at the
tops of the poles. "You must have green
fingers, just like your Granda."

"Will the baby have green fingers
too, Granda?" asked Jody.

"Wait and see,"
said Granda.
"Wait and see."

"It's time to find out what they
taste like," said Granda.

"Oh," said Jody,
"I didn't know we
were going to eat them."

So Jody and Granda picked handfuls
of long thin green beans.

They topped
and tailed them,

sliced and boiled them,

and served them up with butter.

"Mmm!" said Mum. "They're delicious."

The beans grew on and on,

right into the autumn.

Jody picked them every day.

If she missed one, it grew hard and knobbly.

Mum had to cut the stringy edges off.

It didn't taste as nice.

At the end of autumn Granda and Jody
picked the very last beans.

They were the ones right up
at the top of the poles
where Jody couldn't reach.

They were gigantic!

"They're no good,"
said Jody sadly.

"Oh yes they are,"
said Granda.

And he opened them up,
took out the seeds, and spread
the twelve biggest
ones in a circle on
the kitchen table.

"Do you know what these are for, Jody?"
he asked.

"Yes, Granda," said Jody, smiling.
"They're next year's runner beans!"

"And how tall do you think they'll grow?"
asked Granda.

"Wait and see,
Granda,"
said Jody.
"Wait and see."

Index

Look up the pages to find out
about all these bean things.

About the Author

Malachy Doyle lives on the west coast of Wales,
between the mountains and the sea — where, he says,
he grows plants, cats and teenagers.
His favourite sight in the garden is the runner beans
in full flower — a mass of bright scarlet, with the
prospect of tasty meals to come. He recommends
frying the smallest, tenderest beans you can find in
butter and garlic — delicious!

About the Illustrator

Judith Allibone drew inspiration for the white cat in this
story by watching a neighbour's cat playing in the
vegetable patch at the bottom of her garden.
Her own cat is called Myrtle May and
it's black-and-white. This is Judith's first picture book,
and she says that she hopes it will encourage
children to grow things.

NOTES FOR TEACHERS

The READ AND WONDER series is an innovative and versatile resource for reading, thinking and discovery.

Each book invites children to become excited about a topic, see how varied information books can be, and want to find out more.

☞ **Reading aloud** The story form makes these books ideal for reading aloud – in their own right or as part of a cross-curricular topic, to a child or to a whole class. After you've introduced children to the books in this way, they can revisit and enjoy them again and again.

☞ **Shared reading** Big Book editions are available for several titles, so children can read along, discuss the topic, and comment on the different ways information is presented – to wonder together.

☞ **Group and guided reading** Children need to experience a range of reading materials. Information books like these help develop the skills of reading to learn, as part of learning to read. With the support of a reading group, children can become confident, flexible readers.

☞ **Paired reading** It's fun to take turns to read the information in the main text or captions. With a partner, children can explore the pages to satisfy their curiosity and build their understanding.

☞ **Individual reading** These books can be read for interest and pleasure by children at home and in school.

☞ **Research** Once children have been introduced to these books through reading aloud, they can use them for independent or group research, as part of a curricular topic.

☞ **Children's own writing** You can offer these books as strong models for children's own information writing. They can record their observations and findings about a topic, make field notes and sketches, and add extra snippets of information for the reader.

Above all, Read and Wonders are to be enjoyed, and encourage children to develop a lasting curiosity about the world they live in.

Sue Ellis, Centre for Language in Primary Education